John Bunyan's
Poetry

Register This New Book

Benefits of Registering

- ✓ FREE accidental damage replacements
- ✓ FREE audio book – *Pilgrim's Progress*, audiobook edition
- ✓ FREE information about new titles and other freebies

www.anekopress.com/new-book-registration

John Bunyan's
Poetry

Divine Emblems

John Bunyan

Printed in the United States of America
Aneko Press – *Our Readers Matter*[TM]
www.anekopress.com
Aneko Press, Life Sentence Publishing, and our logos are trademarks of Life Sentence Publishing, Inc.
203 E. Birch Street
P.O. Box 652
Abbotsford, WI 54405
POETRY / Subjects & Themes / Inspirational & Religious
Paperback ISBN: 978-1-62245-427-3
eBook ISBN: 978-1-62245-428-0
10 9 8 7 6 5 4 3 2 1
Available where books are sold

Contents

Publisher's Note

While John Bunyan originally wrote this book with children in mind, it will quickly become obvious to the reader that these poems are as relevant to adults as they are to children. Our desire is, whether boy, girl, man, or woman, that all will reap a spiritual blessing as they read and ponder this significant volume by the most-loved John Bunyan. May the Lord lead you in an ever deepening relationship with Him.

I

UPON THE BARREN FIG-TREE IN GOD'S VINEYARD

hat, barren here! in this so good a soil?
The sight of this doth make God's heart recoil
From giving thee his blessing; barren tree,
Bear fruit, or else thine end will cursed be!

Art thou not planted by the water-side?
Know'st not thy Lord by fruit is glorified?
The sentence is, Cut down the barren tree:
Bear fruit, or else thine end will cursed be.

Hast thou been digg'd about and dunged too,
Will neither patience nor yet dressing do?
The executioner is come, O tree,
Bear fruit, or else thine end will cursed be!

He that about thy roots takes pains to dig,
Would, if on thee were found but one good fig,
Preserve thee from the axe: but, barren tree,
Bear fruit, or else thy end will cursed be!

The utmost end of patience is at hand,
'Tis much if thou much longer here doth stand.
O cumber-ground, thou art a barren tree.
Bear fruit, or else thine end will cursed be!

Thy standing nor they name will help at all;
When fruitful trees are spared, thou must fall.
The axe is laid unto thy roots, O tree!
Bear fruit, or else thine end will cursed be.

UPON THE LARK AND THE FOWLER

hou simple bird, what makes thou here to play?
Look, there's the fowler, pr'ythee come away.
Do'st not behold the net? Look there, 'tis spread,
Venture a little further, thou art dead.

Is there not room enough in all the field
For thee to play in, but thou needs must yield
To the deceitful glitt'ring of a glass,
Plac'd betwixt nets, to bring thy death to pass?

Bird, if thou art so much for dazzling light,
Look, there's the sun above thee; dart upright;
Thy nature is to soar up to the sky,
Why wilt thou come down to the nets and die?

Take no heed to the fowler's tempting call;
This whistle, he enchanteth birds withal.
Or if thou see'st a live bird in his net,
Believe she's there, 'cause hence she cannot get.

Look how he tempteth thee with is decoy,
That he may rob thee of thy life, thy joy.
Come, pr'ythee bird, I pr'ythee come away,
Why should this net thee take, when 'scape thou may?

Hadst thou not wings, or were thy feathers pull'd,
Or wast thou blind, or fast asleep wer't lull'd,
The case would somewhat alter, but for thee,
Thy eyes are ope, and thou hast wings to flee.

Remember that thy song is in thy rise,
Not in thy fall; earth's not thy paradise.
Keep up aloft, then, let thy circuits be
Above, where birds from fowler's nets are free.

Comparison

This fowler is an emblem of the devil,
His nets and whistle, figures of all evil.
His glass an emblem is of sinful pleasure,
And his decoy of who counts sin a treasure.

This simple lark's a shadow of a saint,
Under allurings, ready now to faint.
This admonisher a true teacher is,
Whose works to show the soul the snare and bliss,
And how it may this fowler's net escape,
And not commit upon itself this rape.

III

UPON THE VINE-TREE

 hat is the vine, more than another tree?
Nay most, than it, more tall, more comely be.
What workman thence will take a beam or pin,
To make ought which may be delighted in?
Its excellency in its fruit doth lie:
A fruitless vine, it is not worth a fly.

Comparison

What are professors more than other men?
Nothing at all. Nay, there's not one in ten,
Either for wealth, or wit, that may compare,
In many things, with some that carnal are.
Good are they, if they mortify their sin,
But without that, they are not worth a pin.

IV

MEDITATIONS UPON AN EGG

The egg's no chick by falling from the hen;
Nor man a Christian, till he's born again.

The egg's at first contained in the shell;
Men, afore grace, in sins and darkness dwell.
The egg, when laid, by warmth is made a chicken,
And Christ, by grace, those dead in sin doth quicken.
The egg, when first a chick, the shell's its prison;
So's flesh to the soul, who yet with Christ is risen.
The shell doth crack, the chick doth chirp and peep,

The flesh decays, as men do pray and weep.
The shell doth break, the chick's at liberty,
The flesh falls off, the soul mounts up on high
But both do not enjoy the self-same plight;
The soul is safe, the chick now fears the kite.

But chicks from rotten eggs do not proceed,
Nor is a hypocrite a saint indeed.
The rotten egg, though underneath the hen,
If crack'd, stinks, and is loathsome unto men.
Nor doth her warmth make what is rotten sound;
What's rotten, rotten will at last be found.
The hypocrite, sin has him in possession,
He is a rotten egg under profession.

Some eggs bring cockatrices; and some men
Seem hatch'd and brooded in the viper's den.
Some eggs bring wild-fowls; and some men there be
As wild as are the wildest fowls that flee.
Some eggs bring spiders, and some men appear
More venom'd than the worst of spiders are.[1]
Some eggs bring piss-ants,[2] and some seem to me
As much for trifles as the piss-ants be.
Thus divers eggs do produce divers shapes,
As like some men as monkeys are like apes.
But this is but an egg, were it a chick,
Here had been legs, and wings, and bones to pick.

---

1   Spiders being venomous was a vulgar error, universally believed,
     until modern discoveries have proved the contrary, excepting a few
     foreign species.—Ed.
2   Originates from the word *pismire*, a 14th-century term for ant.

V

OF FOWLS FLYING IN THE AIR

ethinks I see a sight most excellent,
All sorts of birds fly in the firmament:
Some great, some small, all of a divers kind,
Mine eye affecting, pleasant to my mind.
Look how they tumble in the wholesome air,
Above the world of worldlings, and their care.
And as they divers are in bulk and hue,
So are they in their way of flying too.
So many birds, so many various things
Tumbling in the element upon their wings.

Comparison

These birds are emblems of those men that shall
Ere long possess the heavens, their all in all.
They are each of a diverse shape and kind,
To teach we of all nations there shall find.
They are some great, some little, as we see,
To show some great, some small, in glory be.[3]
Their flying diversely, as we behold,
Do show saints' joys will there be manifold;
Some glide, some mount, some flutter, and some do,
In a mix'd way of flying, glory too.
And all to show each saint, to his content,
Shall roll and tumble in that firmament.

---

3   This is a scriptural idea of the inhabitants of heaven. Revelation
11:8, saints 'small and great.' Matthew 19:28: 'The Son of man on
his throne, and the twelve apostles on their thrones.' Revelation
4:10: 'Four and twenty elders on their thrones.' Revelation 5:11: 'An
innumerable company of worshippers.'—Ed.

VI

UPON THE LORD'S PRAYER

ur Father which in heaven art,
Thy name be always hallowed;
Thy kingdom come, thy will be done;
Thy heavenly path be followed
By us on earth as 'tis with thee,
We humbly pray;
And let our bread us given be,
From day to day.

Forgive our debts as we forgive
Those that to us indebted are:
Into temptation lead us not,[4]
But save us from the wicked snare.
The kingdom's thine, the power too,
We thee adore;
The glory also shall be thine
For evermore.

---

4 In an ancient battledore or horn-book, and in one of Henry VIII's
  primers, both in the editor's possession, this sentence is translated—
  'And let us not be led into temptation.'—Ed.

VII

MEDITATIONS UPON PEEP OF DAY

 oft, though it be peep of day, don't know
Whether 'tis night, whether 'tis day or no.
I fancy that I see a little light,
But cannot yet distinguish day from night;
I hope, I doubt, but steady yet I be not,
I am not at a point, the sun I see not.
Thus 'tis with such who grace but now[5] possest,
They know not yet if they be cursed or blest.

---

5   When divine light first dawns upon the soul, and reveals sin, O
    how difficult is it to conclude that sin is pardoned, and the sinner
    blest!—Ed.

VIII

UPON THE FLINT IN THE WATER

his flint, time out of mind, has there abode,
Where crystal streams make their continual
road.
Yet it abides a flint as much as 'twere
Before it touched the water, or came there

Its hard obdurateness is not abated,
'Tis not at all by water penetrated.
Though water hath a soft'ning virtue in't,
This stone it can't dissolve, for 'tis a flint.

Yea, though it in the water doth remain,
It doth its fiery nature still retain.
If you oppose it with its opposite,
At you, yea, in your face, its fire 'twill spit.

Comparison

This flint an emblem is of those that lie,
Like stones, under the Word, until they die.
Its crystal streams have not their nature changed,
They are not, from their lusts, by grace estranged.

IX

UPON THE FISH IN THE WATER

he water is the fish's element;
Take her from thence, none can her death
    prevent;
And some have said, who have transgressors been,
As good not be, as to be kept from sin.

The water is the fish's element:
Leave her but there, and she is well content.
So's he, who in the path of life doth plod,
Take all, says he, let me but have my God.

The water is the fish's element,
Her sportings there to her are excellent;
So is God's service unto holy men,
They are not in their element till then.

X

UPON THE SWALLOW

his pretty bird, O! how she flies and sings,[6]
But could she do so if she had not wings?
Her wings bespeak my faith, her songs my
      peace;
When I believe and sing my doubtings cease.

---

6   The swallow is remarkably swift in flight; 'their note is a slight
    twittering, which they seldom if ever exert but upon the wing.'—
    Goldsmith's Natural History.—Ed.

XI

UPON THE BEE

he bee goes out, and honey home doth bring,
And some who seek that honey find a sting.
Now would'st thou have the honey, and be free
From stinging, in the first place kill the bee.

Comparison

This bee an emblem truly is of sin,
Whose sweet, unto a many, death hath been.
Now would'st have sweet from sin and yet not die,
Do thou it, in the first place, mortify.

XII

UPON A LOWERING MORNING

Well, with the day I see the clouds appear,
And mix the light with darkness everywhere;
This threatening is, to travellers that go
Long journeys, slabby rain they'll have, or snow.
Else, while I gaze, the sun doth with his beams
Belace the clouds, as 'twere with bloody streams;
This done, they suddenly do watery grow,
And weep, and pour their tears out where they go.

Comparison

Thus 'tis when gospel light doth usher in
To us both sense of grace and sense of sin;
Yea, when it makes sin red with Christ's blood,
Then we can weep till weeping does us good.

XIII

UPON OVER-MUCH NICENESS

Tis much to see how over nice some are
About the body and household affair,
While what's of worth they slightly pass it by,
Not doing, or doing it slovenly.

Their house must be well furnished, be in print,[7]
Meanwhile their soul lies ley,[8] has no good in't.

---

7   'Be in print'; a proverbial expression, to show order and regularity;
     like type in print.—Ed.
8   'Ley'; barren or fallow, uncultivated, generally spelt lea.—Ed.

Its outside also they must beautify,
When in it there's scarce common honesty.

Their bodies they must have tricked up and trim,
Their inside full of filth up to the brim.
Upon their clothes there must not be a spot,
But is their lives more than one common blot.

How nice, how coy are some about their diet,
That can their crying souls with hogs'-meat quiet.
All drest must to a hair be, else 'tis naught,
While of the living bread they have no thought.
Thus for their outside they are clean and nice,
While their poor inside stinks with sin and vice.

XIV

MEDITATIONS UPON A CANDLE

an's like a candle in a candlestick,
Made up of tallow and a little wick;
And as the candle when it is not lighted,
So is he who is in his sins benighted.
Nor can a man his soul with grace inspire,
More than can candles set themselves on fire.

Candles receive their light from what they are not;
Men grace from Him for whom at first they care not.
We manage candles when they take the fire;
God men, when he with grace doth them inspire.

And biggest candles give the better light,
As grace on biggest sinners shines most bright.
The candle shines to make another see,
A saint unto his neighbour light should be.
The blinking candle we do much despise,
Saints dim of light are high in no man's eyes.

Again, though it may seem to some a riddle,
We use to light our candles at the middle.[9]
True light doth at the candle's end appear,
And grace the heart first reaches by the ear.
But 'tis the wick the fire doth kindle on,
As 'tis the heart that grace first works upon.
Thus both do fasten upon what's the main,
And so their life and vigour do maintain.

The tallow makes the wick yield to the fire,
And sinful flesh doth make the soul desire
That grace may kindle on it, in it burn;
So evil makes the soul from evil turn.[10]

But candles in the wind are apt to flare,
And Christians, in a tempest, to despair.
The flame also with smoke attended is,
And in our holy lives there's much amiss.

Sometimes a thief will candle-light annoy,
And lusts do seek our graces to destroy.

---

9   This riddle is solved in the fourth line following. The light of the
     fear and love of God begins in the middle of our bodily frame, with
     the heart. Bunyan's love of religious riddles is seen in the second
     part of the Pilgrimage, when Christian is resting at the house of
     Gaius.—Ed.
10   Convictions of sin make the soul turn from sin.—Ed.

What brackish is will make a candle sputter;
'Twixt sin and grace there's oft' a heavy clutter.
Sometimes the light burns dim, 'cause of the snuff,
Sometimes it is blown quite out with a puff;
But watchfulness preventeth both these evils,
Keeps candles light, and grace in spite of devils.

Nor let not snuffs nor puffs make us to doubt,
Our candles may be lighted, though puffed out.
The candle in the night doth all excel,
Nor sun, nor moon, nor stars, then shine so well.
So is the Christian in our hemisphere,
Whose light shows others how their course to steer.
When candles are put out, all's in confusion;
Where Christians are not, devils make intrusion.
Then happy are they who such candles have,
All others dwell in darkness and the grave.
But candles that do blink within the socket,
And saints, whose eyes are always in their pocket,
Are much alike; such candles make us fumble,
And at such saints good men and bad do stumble.[11]

Good candles don't offend, except sore eyes,
Nor hurt, unless it be the silly flies.
Thus none like burning candles in the night,
Nor ought[12] to holy living for delight.
But let us draw towards the candle's end:
The fire, you see, doth wick and tallow spend,

---

11   This character is admirably drawn in the second part of the Pilgrim's
      Progress—Mr. Brisk, a suitor to Mercy.—Ed.
12   Preterite of the verb 'to save,' from the Saxon agan, to be held or
      bound by moral obligation.—Imperial Dictionary.—Ed.

As grace man's life until his glass is run,
And so the candle and the man is done.

The man now lays him down upon his bed,
The wick yields up its fire, and so is dead.
The candle now extinct is, but the man
By grace mounts up to glory, there to stand.

XV

UPON THE SACRAMENTS

wo sacraments I do believe there be,
Baptism and the Supper of the Lord;
Both mysteries divine, which do to me,
By God's appointment, benefit afford.
But shall they be my God, or shall I have
Of them so foul and impious a thought,
To think that from the curse they can me save?
Bread, wine, nor water, me no ransom bought.[13]

---

13 What folly, nay, madness, for man to pretend to make God of a little
flour, or to rely for forgiveness of sin on a wafer, a bit of bread, or
a little wine or water. How degraded is he that pretends to believe
such palpable absurdities.—Ed.

XVI

UPON THE SUN'S REFLECTION UPON THE CLOUDS IN A FAIR MORNING

ook yonder, ah! methinks mine eyes do see
Clouds edged with silver, as fine garments be;
They look as if they saw that golden face
That makes black clouds most beautiful with grace.
Unto the saints' sweet incense, or their prayer,
These smoky curdled clouds I do compare.
For as these clouds seem edged, or laced with gold,
Their prayers return with blessings manifold.

XVII

UPON APPAREL

God gave us clothes to hide our nakedness,
And we by them do it expose to view.
Our pride and unclean minds to an excess,
By our apparel, we to others show.[14]

---

14   This is one of Bunyan's keen, shrewd, home thrusts. Clothes profess-
      edly made to hide what they studiously display!!—Ed.

XVIII

THE SINNER AND THE SPIDER

Sinner
What black, what ugly crawling thing art thou?

Spider
I am a spider——————————

Sinner
A spider, ay, also a filthy creature.

Spider

Not filthy as thyself in name or feature.
My name entailed is to my creation,
My features from the God of thy salvation.

Sinner

I am a man, and in God's image made,
I have a soul shall neither die nor fade,
God has possessed me[15] with human reason,
Speak not against me lest thou speakest treason.
For if I am the image of my Maker,
Of slanders laid on me He is partaker.

Spider

I know thou art a creature far above me,
Therefore I shun, I fear, and also love thee.
But though thy God hath made thee such a creature,
Thou hast against him often played the traitor.
Thy sin has fetched thee down: leave off to boast;
Nature thou hast defiled, God's image lost.
Yea, thou thyself a very beast hast made,
And art become like grass, which soon doth fade.
Thy soul, thy reason, yea, thy spotless state,
Sin has subjected to th' most dreadful fate.
But I retain my primitive condition,
I've all but what I lost by thy ambition.

Sinner

Thou venomed thing, I know not what to call thee,

---

15   Possessed me with, or has given me possession of.—Ed.

The dregs of nature surely did befall thee,
Thou wast made of the dross and scum of all,
Man hates thee; doth, in scorn, thee spider call.

Spider

My venom's good for something, 'cause God made it,
Thy sin hath spoiled thy nature, doth degrade it.
Of human virtues, therefore, though I fear thee,
I will not, though I might, despise and jeer thee.
Thou say'st I am the very dregs of nature,
Thy sin's the spawn of devils, 'tis no creature.
Thou say'st man hates me 'cause I am a spider,
Poor man, thou at thy God art a derider;
My venom tendeth to my preservation,
Thy pleasing follies work out thy damnation.
Poor man, I keep the rules of my creation,
Thy sin has cast thee headlong from thy station.
I hurt nobody willingly, but thou
Art a self-murderer; thou know'st not how
To do what good is; no, thou lovest evil;
Thou fliest God's law, adherest to the devil.[16]

Sinner

Ill-shaped creature, there's antipathy
'Twixt man and spiders, 'tis in vain to lie;
I hate thee, stand off, if thou dost come nigh me,
I'll crush thee with my foot; I do defy thee.

---

16   Man's sinfulness, by nature and practice, justly, but awfully
     described.—Mason.

Spider

They are ill-shaped, who warped are by sin,
Antipathy in thee hath long time been
To God; no marvel, then, if me, his creature,
Thou dost defy, pretending name and feature.
But why stand off? My presence shall not throng thee,
'Tis not my venom, but thy sin doth wrong thee.

Come, I will teach thee wisdom, do but hear me,
I was made for thy profit, do not fear me.
But if thy God thou wilt not hearken to,
What can the swallow, ant, or spider do?
Yet I will speak, I can but be rejected,
Sometimes great things by small means are effected.

Hark, then, though man is noble by creation,
He's lapsed now to such degeneration,
Is so besotted and so careless grown,
As not to grieve though he has overthrown
Himself, and brought to bondage everything
Created, from the spider to the king.
This we poor sensitives do feel and see;
For subject to the curse you made us be.
Tread not upon me, neither from me go;
'Tis man which has brought all the world to woe,

The law of my creation bids me teach thee;
I will not for thy pride to God impeach thee.
I spin, I weave, and all to let thee see,
Thy best performances but cobwebs be.
Thy glory now is brought to such an ebb,
It doth not much excel the spider's web;

My webs becoming snares and traps for flies,
Do set the wiles of hell before thine eyes;
Their tangling nature is to let thee see,
Thy sins too of a tangling nature be.
My den, or hole, for that 'tis bottomless,
Doth of damnation show the lastingness.
My lying quiet until the fly is catch'd,
Shows secretly hell hath thy ruin hatch'd.
In that I on her seize, when she is taken,
I show who gathers whom God hath forsaken.
The fly lies buzzing in my web to tell
Thee how the sinners roar and howl in hell.

Now, since I show thee all these mysteries,
How canst thou hate me, or me scandalize?

Sinner

Well, well; I no more will be a derider,
I did not look for such things from a spider.

Spider

Come, hold thy peace; what I have yet to say,
If heeded, help thee may another day.
Since I an ugly ven'mous creature be,
There is some semblance 'twixt vile man and me.
My wild and heedless runnings are like those
Whose ways to ruin do their souls expose.
Daylight is not my time, I work in th' night,
To show they are like me who hate the light.
The maid sweeps one web down, I make another,
To show how heedless ones convictions smother;

My web is no defence at all to me,
Nor will false hopes at judgment be to thee.

Sinner

O spider, I have heard thee, and do wonder
A spider should thus lighten and thus thunder.

Spider

Do but hold still, and I will let thee see
Yet in my ways more mysteries there be.
Shall not I do thee good, if I thee tell,
I show to thee a four-fold way to hell;
For, since I set my web in sundry places,
I show men go to hell in divers traces.

One I set in the window, that I might
Show some go down to hell with gospel light.
One I set in a corner, as you see,
To show how some in secret snared be.
Gross webs great store I set in darksome places,
To show how many sin with brazen faces;
Another web I set aloft on high,
To show there's some professing men must die.
Thus in my ways God wisdom doth conceal,
And by my ways that wisdom doth reveal.

I hide myself when I for flies do wait,
So doth the devil when he lays his bait;
If I do fear the losing of my prey,
I stir me, and more snares upon her lay:
This way and that her wings and legs I tie,

That, sure as she is catch'd, so she must die.
But if I see she's like to get away,
Then with my venom I her journey stay.
All which my ways the devil imitates
To catch men, 'cause he their salvation hates.

Sinner

O spider, thou delight'st me with thy skill!
I pr'ythee spit this venom at me still.

Spider

I am a spider, yet I can possess
The palace of a king, where happiness
So much abounds. Nor when I do go thither,
Do they ask what, or whence I come, or whither
I make my hasty travels; no, not they;
They let me pass, and I go on my way.
I seize the palace,[17] do with hands take hold
Of doors, of locks, or bolts; yea, I am bold,
When in, to clamber up unto the throne,
And to possess it, as if 'twere mine own.
Nor is there any law forbidding me
Here to abide, or in this palace be.

Yea, if I please, I do the highest stories
Ascend, there sit, and so behold the glories
Myself is compassed with, as if I were
One of the chiefest courtiers that be there.

---

17   See Proverbs 30:20, and Pilgrim's Progress. There is also a very
     striking allusion to the subject of this emblem, in Bunyan's Light
     in Darkness.

Here lords and ladies do come round about me,
With grave demeanour, nor do any flout me
For this, my brave adventure, no, not they;
They come, they go, but leave me there to stay.

Now, my reproacher, I do by all this
Show how thou may'st possess thyself of bliss:
Thou art worse than a spider, but take hold
On Christ the door, thou shalt not be controll'd.
By him do thou the heavenly palace enter;
None chide thee will for this thy brave adventure;
Approach thou then unto the very throne,
There speak thy mind, fear not, the day's thine own;
Nor saint, nor angel, will thee stop or stay,
But rather tumble blocks out of the way.
My venom stops not me; let not thy vice
Stop thee; possess thyself of paradise.

Go on, I say, although thou be a sinner,
Learn to be bold in faith, of me a spinner.
This is the way the glories to possess,
And to enjoy what no man can express.

Sometimes I find the palace door uplock'd,
And so my entrance thither has upblock'd.
But am I daunted? No, I here and there
Do feel and search; so if I anywhere,
At any chink or crevice, find my way,
I crowd, I press for passage, make no stay.
And so through difficulty I attain
The palace; yea, the throne where princes reign.
I crowd sometimes, as if I'd burst in sunder;

And art thou crushed with striving, do not wonder.
Some scarce get in, and yet indeed they enter;
Knock, for they nothing have, that nothing venture.

Nor will the King himself throw dirt on thee,
As thou hast cast reproaches upon me.
He will not hate thee, O thou foul backslider!
As thou didst me, because I am a spider.
Now, to conclude since I such doctrine bring,
Slight me no more, call me not ugly thing.
God wisdom hath unto the piss-ant given,
And spiders may teach men the way to heaven.

Sinner

Well, my good spider, I my errors see,
I was a fool for railing upon thee.
Thy nature, venom, and thy fearful hue,
Both show that sinners are, and what they do.
Thy way and works do also darkly tell,
How some men go to heaven, and some to hell.
Thou art my monitor, I am a fool;
They learn may, that to spiders go to school.

MEDITATIONS UPON THE DAY BEFORE THE SUN-RISING

 ut all this while, where's he whose golden rays
Drives night away and beautifies our days?
Where's he whose goodly face doth warm and heal,
And show us what the darksome nights conceal?
Where's he that thaws our ice, drives cold away?
Let's have him, or we care not for the day.

Thus 'tis with who partakers are of grace,
There's nought to them like their Redeemer's face.

XX

OF THE MOLE IN THE GROUND

he mole's a creature very smooth and slick,
She digs i' th' dirt, but 'twill not on her stick;
So's he who counts this world his greatest gains,
Yet nothing gets but's labour for his pains.
Earth's the mole's element, she can't abide
To be above ground, dirt heaps are her pride;
And he is like her who the worldling plays,
He imitates her in her work and ways.

Poor silly mole, that thou should'st love to be
Where thou nor sun, nor moon, nor stars can see.
But O! how silly's he who doth not care
So he gets earth, to have of heaven a share!

XXI

OF THE CUCKOO

Thou booby, say'st thou nothing but Cuckoo?
The robin and the wren can thee outdo.
They to us play through their little throats,
Taking not one, but sundry pretty taking notes.
But thou hast fellows, some like thee can do
Little but suck our eggs, and sing Cuckoo.

Thy notes do not first welcome in our spring,
Nor dost thou its first tokens to us bring.

Birds less than thee by far, like prophets, do
Tell us, 'tis coming, though not by Cuckoo.

Nor dost thou summer have away with thee,
Though thou a yawling bawling Cuckoo be.
When thou dost cease among us to appear,
Then doth our harvest bravely crown our year.
But thou hast fellows, some like thee can do
Little but suck our eggs, and sing Cuckoo.

Since Cuckoos forward not our early spring,
Nor help with notes to bring our harvest in;
And since, while here, she only makes a noise,
So pleasing unto none as girls and boys,
The Formalist we may compare her to,
For he doth suck our eggs, and sing Cuckoo.

XXII

OF THE BOY AND BUTTERFLY

ehold how eager this our little boy
Is for this Butterfly, as if all joy,
All profits, honours, yea, and lasting pleasures,
Were wrapt up in her, or the richest treasures,
Found in her, would be bundled up together,
When all her all is lighter than a feather.

He halloos, runs, and cries out, Here, boys, here,
Nor doth he brambles or the nettles fear.
He stumbles at the mole-hills, up he gets,

And runs again, as one bereft of wits;
And all this labour and this large outcry,
Is only for a silly butterfly.

Comparison

This little boy an emblem is of those
Whose hearts are wholly at the world's dispose,
The butterfly doth represent to me,
The world's best things at best but fading be.
All are but painted nothings and false joys,
Like this poor butterfly to these our boys.
His running through nettles, thorns, and briars,
To gratify his boyish fond desires;
His tumbling over mole-hills to attain
His end, namely, his butterfly to gain;
Doth plainly show what hazards some men run.
To get what will be lost as soon as won.
Men seem in choice, than children far more wise,
Because they run not after butterflies;
When yet, alas! for what are empty toys,
They follow children, like to beardless boys.[18]

---

18   He who, in riper years, seeks happiness in sensual gratification, is
     a child in understanding: he only changes his toys.—Ed.

XXIII

OF THE FLY AT THE CANDLE

hat ails this fly thus desperately to enter
A combat with the candle? Will she venture
To clash at light? Away, thou silly fly;
Thus doing thou wilt burn thy wings and die.

But 'tis a folly her advice to give,
She'll kill the candle, or she will not live.
Slap, says she, at it; then she makes retreat,
So wheels about, and doth her blows repeat.

Nor doth the candle let her quite escape,
But gives some little check unto the ape:
Throws up her heels it doth, so down she falls,
Where she lies sprawling, and for succour calls.

When she recovers, up she gets again,
And at the candle comes with might and main,
But now behold, the candle takes the fly,
And holds her, till she doth by burning die.

Comparison

This candle is an emblem of that light
Our gospel gives in this our darksome night.
The fly a lively picture is of those
That hate and do this gospel light oppose.
At last the gospel doth become their snare,
Doth them with burning hands in pieces tear.[19]

---

19 'To the one, a savour of death unto death; and to the other, a savour
of life unto life' (2 Cor 2:16).

XXIV

ON THE RISING OF THE SUN

ook, look, brave Sol doth peep up from beneath,
Shows us his golden face, doth on us breathe;
He also doth compass us round with glories,
Whilst he ascends up to his highest stories.
Where he his banner over us displays,
And gives us light to see our works and ways.

Nor are we now, as at the peep of light,
To question, is it day, or is it night?

The night is gone, the shadows fled away,
And we now most sure are that it is day.
Our eyes behold it, and our hearts believe it;
Nor can the wit of man in this deceive it.

And thus it is when Jesus shows his face,
And doth assure us of his love and grace.

XXV

UPON THE PROMISING
FRUITFULNESS OF A TREE

A comely sight indeed it is to see
A world of blossoms on an apple-tree:
Yet far more comely would this tree appear,
If all its dainty blooms young apples were.
But how much more might one upon it see,
If all would hang there till they ripe should be.
But most of all in beauty 'twould abound,
If then none worm-eaten should there be found.

But we, alas! do commonly behold
Blooms fall apace, if mornings be but cold.
They too, which hang till they young apples are,
By blasting winds and vermin take despair,
Store that do hang, while almost ripe, we see
By blust'ring winds are shaken from the tree,
So that of many, only some there be,
That grow till they come to maturity.

Comparison

This tree a perfect emblem is of those
Which God doth plant, which in his garden grows,
Its blasted blooms are motions unto good,
Which chill affections do nip in the bud.

Those little apples which yet blasted are,
Show some good purposes, no good fruits bear.
Those spoiled by vermin are to let us see,
How good attempts by bad thoughts ruin'd be.

Those which the wind blows down, while they are green,
Show good works have by trials spoiled been.
Those that abide, while ripe upon the tree,
Show, in a good man, some ripe fruit will be.

Behold then how abortive some fruits are,
Which at the first most promising appear.
The frost, the wind, the worm, with time doth show,
There flows, from much appearance, works but few.

XXVI

UPON THE THIEF

The thief, when he doth steal, thinks he doth gain;
Yet then the greatest loss he doth sustain.
Come, thief, tell me thy gains, but do not falter.
When summ'd, what comes it to more than the halter?

Perhaps, thou'lt say, The halter I defy;
So thou may'st say, yet by the halter die.
Thou'lt say, Then there's an end; no, pr'ythee, hold,
He was no friend of thine that thee so told.

Hear thou the Word of God, that will thee tell,
Without repentance thieves must go to hell.

But should it be as thy false prophet says,
Yet nought but loss doth come by thievish ways.

All honest men will flee thy company,
Thou liv'st a rogue, and so a rogue will die.
Innocent boldness thou hast none at all,
Thy inward thoughts do thee a villain call.

Sometimes when thou liest warmly on thy bed,
Thou art like one unto the gallows led.
Fear, as a constable, breaks in upon thee,
Thou art as if the town was up to stone thee.

If hogs do grunt, or silly rats do rustle,
Thou art in consternation, think'st a bustle
By men about the door, is made to take thee,
And all because good conscience doth forsake thee.

Thy case is most deplorably so bad,
Thou shunn'st to think on't, lest thou should'st be mad.
Thou art beset with mischiefs every way,
The gallows groaneth for thee every day.

Wherefore, I pr'ythee, thief, thy theft forbear,
Consult thy safety, pr'ythee, have a care.
If once thy head be got within the noose,
'Twill be too late a longer life to choose.

As to the penitent thou readest of,
What's that to them who at repentance scoff.
Nor is that grace at thy command or power,
That thou should'st put it off till the last hour.
I pr'ythee, thief, think on't, and turn betime;
Few go to life who do the gallows climb.

XXVII

OF THE CHILD WITH THE
BIRD AT THE BUSH

y little bird, how canst thou sit
And sing amidst so many thorns?
Let me a hold upon thee get,
My love with honour thee adorns.

Thou art at present little worth,
Five farthings none will give for thee,
But pr'ythee, little bird, come forth,
Thou of more value art to me.

'Tis true it is sunshine to-day,
To-morrow birds will have a storm;
My pretty one come thou away,
My bosom then shall keep thee warm.

Thou subject are to cold o'nights,
When darkness is thy covering;
At days thy danger's great by kites,
How can'st thou then sit there and sing?

Thy food is scarce and scanty too,
'Tis worms and trash which thou dost eat;
Thy present state I pity do,
Come, I'll provide thee better meat.

I'll feed thee with white bread and milk,
And sugar plums, if them thou crave.
I'll cover thee with finest silk,
That from the cold I may thee save.

My father's palace shall be thine,
Yea, in it thou shalt sit and sing;
My little bird, if thou'lt be mine,
The whole year round shall be thy spring.

I'll teach thee all the notes at court,
Unthought-of music thou shalt play;
And all that thither do resort,
Shall praise thee for it every day.

I'll keep thee safe from cat and cur,
No manner o' harm shall come to thee;
Yea, I will be thy succourer,
My bosom shall thy cabin be.

But lo, behold, the bird is gone;
These charmings would not make her yield;
The child's left at the bush alone,
The bird flies yonder o'er the field.

Comparison

This child of Christ an emblem is,
The bird to sinners I compare,
The thorns are like those sins of his
Which do surround him everywhere.

Her songs, her food, and sunshine day,
Are emblems of those foolish toys,
Which to destruction lead the way,
The fruit of worldly, empty joys.

The arguments this child doth choose
To draw to him a bird thus wild,
Shows Christ familiar speech doth use
To make's to him be reconciled.

The bird in that she takes her wing,
To speed her from him after all,
Shows us vain man loves any thing
Much better than the heavenly call.

XXVIII

OF MOSES AND HIS WIFE

This Moses was a fair and comely man,
His wife a swarthy Ethiopian;
Nor did his milk-white bosom change her sin.
She came out thence as black as she went in.
Now Moses was a type of Moses' law,
His wife likewise of one that never saw
Another way unto eternal life;
There's mystery, then, in Moses and his wife.

The law is very holy, just, and good,
And to it is espoused all flesh and blood;
But this its goodness it cannot bestow
On any that are wedded thereunto.

Therefore as Moses' wife came swarthy in,
And went out from him without change of skin,
So he that doth the law for life adore,
Shall yet by it be left a black-a-more.

XXIX

OF THE ROSE-BUSH

his homely bush doth to mine eyes expose
A very fair, yea, comely ruddy rose.
This rose doth also bow its head to me,
Saying, Come, pluck me, I thy rose will be;
Yet offer I to gather rose or bud,
Ten to one but the bush will have my blood.

This looks like a trapan,[20] or a decoy,
To offer, and yet snap, who would enjoy;

---

20   'Trapan' is the Saxon verb to ensnare, modernized to trap.—Ed.

Yea, the more eager on't, the more in danger,
Be he the master of it, or a stranger.

Bush, why dost bear a rose if none must have it.
Who dost expose it, yet claw those that crave it?
Art become freakish? dost the wanton play,
Or doth thy testy humour tend its way?

Comparison

This rose God's Son is, with his ruddy looks.
But what's the bush, whose pricks, like tenter-hooks,
Do scratch and claw the finest lady's hands,
Or rend her clothes, if she too near it stands?

This bush an emblem is of Adam's race,
Of which Christ came, when he his Father's grace
Commended to us in his crimson blood,
While he in sinners' stead and nature stood.

Thus Adam's race did bear this dainty rose,
And doth the same to Adam's race expose;
But those of Adam's race which at it catch,
Adam's race will them prick, and claw, and scratch.

XXX

OF THE GOING DOWN
OF THE SUN

hat, hast thou run thy race, art going down?
Thou seemest angry, why dost on us frown?
Yea, wrap thy head with clouds and hide thy
   face,
As threatening to withdraw from us thy grace?

O leave us not! When once thou hid'st thy head,
Our horizon with darkness will be spread.
Tell who hath thee offended, turn again.
Alas! too late, intreaties are in vain.

Comparison

Our gospel has had here a summer's day,
But in its sunshine we, like fools, did play;
Or else fall out, and with each other wrangle,
And did, instead of work, not much but jangle.

And if our sun seems angry, hides his face,
Shall it go down, shall night possess this place?
Let not the voice of night birds us afflict,
And of our misspent summer us convict.[21]

---

21   How agonizing will be the cry of the lost soul—'The harvest is past,
     the summer is ended, and we are not saved' (Jer 8:20).—Ed. Upon
     the brittle thread of life hang everlasting things.—Mason.

XXXI

UPON THE FROG

he frog by nature is both damp and cold,
Her mouth is large, her belly much will hold;
She sits somewhat ascending, loves to be
Croaking in gardens, though unpleasantly.

Comparison

The hypocrite is like unto this frog,
As like as is the puppy to the dog.
He is of nature cold, his mouth is wide

To prate, and at true goodness to deride.
He mounts his head as if he was above
The world, when yet 'tis that which has his love.
And though he seeks in churches for to croak,
He neither loveth Jesus nor his yoke.

XXXII

UPON THE WHIPPING OF A TOP

is with the whip the boy sets up the top,
The whip makes it run round upon its toe;
The whip makes it hither and thither hop:
'Tis with the whip the top is made to go.

Comparison

Our legalist is like unto this top,
Without a whip he doth not duty do;
Let Moses whip him, he will skip and hop;
Forbear to whip, he'll neither stand nor go.

XXXIII

UPON THE ANT

ust we unto the ant go to school,
To learn of her in summer to provide
For winter next ensuing. Man's a fool,
Or silly ants would not be made his guide.
But, sluggard, is it not a shame for thee
To be outdone by ant? Pr'ythee hear:
Their works, too, will thy condemnation be
When at the judgment-seat thou shalt appear.
But since thy God doth bid thee to her go,
Obey, her ways consider, and be wise;
The ant tell thee will what thou must do,
And set the way to life before thine eyes.

XXXIV

UPON THE BEGGAR

He wants, he asks, he pleads his poverty,
They within doors do him an alms deny.
He doth repeat and aggravate his grief,
But they repulse him, give him no relief.

He begs, they say, Begone; he will not hear,
But coughs, sighs, and makes signs he still is there;
They disregard him, he repeats his groans;
They still say nay, and he himself bemoans.
They grow more rugged, they call him vagrant;

He cries the shriller, trumpets out his want.
At last, when they perceive he'll take no nay,
An alms they give him without more delay.

Comparison

This beggar doth resemble them that pray
To God for mercy, and will take no nay,
But wait, and count that all his hard gainsays
Are nothing else but fatherly delays;
Then imitate him, praying souls, and cry:
There's nothing like to importunity.

XXXV

UPON THE HORSE AND HIS RIDER

There's one rides very sagely on the road,
Showing that he affects the gravest mode.
Another rides tantivy, or full trot,
To show much gravity he matters not.

Lo, here comes one amain, he rides full speed,
Hedge, ditch, nor miry bog, he doth not heed.
One claws it up-hill without stop or check,
Another down as if he'd break his neck.
Now every horse has his especial guider;
Then by his going you may know the rider.

Comparison

Now let us turn our horse into a man,
His rider to a spirit, if we can.
Then let us, by the methods of the guider,
Tell every horse how he should know his rider.

Some go, as men, direct in a right way,
Nor are they suffered to go astray;
As with a bridle they are governed,
And kept from paths which lead unto the dead.

Now this good man has his especial guider,
Then by his going let him know his rider.

Some go as if they did not greatly care,
Whether of heaven or hell they should be heir.
The rein, it seems, is laid upon their neck,
They seem to go their way without a check.

Now this man too has his especial guider,
And by his going he may know his rider.

Some again run as if resolved to die,
Body and soul, to all eternity.
Good counsel they by no means can abide;
They'll have their course whatever them betide.

Now these poor men have their especial guider,
Were they not fools they soon might know their rider.

There's one makes head against all godliness,
Those too, that do profess it, he'll distress;
He'll taunt and flout if goodness doth appear,
And at its countenancers mock and jeer.

Now this man, too, has his especial guider,
And by his going he might know his rider.

XXXVI

UPON THE SIGHT OF A POUND OF CANDLES FALLING TO THE GROUND

ut be the candles down, and scattered too,
Some lying here, some there? What shall we do?
Hold, light the candle there that stands on high,
It you may find the other candles by.
Light that, I say, and so take up the pound
You did let fall and scatter on the ground.

Comparison

The fallen candles do us intimate
The bulk of God's elect in their laps'd state;
Their lying scattered in the dark may be
To show, by man's lapsed state, his misery.

The candle that was taken down and lighted,
Thereby to find them fallen and benighted,
Is Jesus Christ; God, by his light, doth gather
Who he will save, and be unto a Father.

XXXVII

UPON A PENNY LOAF

Thy price one penny is in time of plenty,
In famine doubled, 'tis from one to twenty.
Yea, no man knows what price on thee to set
When there is but one penny loaf to get.

Comparison

This loaf's an emblem of the Word of God,
A thing of low esteem before the rod
Of famine smites the soul with fear of death,
But then it is our all, our life, our breath.[22]

---

22 When the Word of God dwells in us richly in all wisdom, then will
the peace of God rule in our hearts, and we shall be sweetly inclined
to every good thought, word, and work.—Ed.

XXXVIII

THE BOY AND WATCHMAKER

his watch my father did on me bestow,
A golden one it is, but 'twill not go,
Unless it be at an uncertainty:
But as good none as one to tell a lie.

When 'tis high day my hand will stand at nine;
I think there's no man's watch so bad as mine.
Sometimes 'tis sullen, 'twill not go at all,
And yet 'twas never broke nor had a fall.

Watchmaker.

Your watch, though it be good, through want of skill
May fail to do according to your will.
Suppose the balance, wheels, and springs be good,
And all things else, unless you understood
To manage it, as watches ought to be,
Your watch will still be at uncertainty.
Come, tell me, do you keep it from the dust,
Yea, wind it also duly up you must?
Take heed, too, that you do not strain the spring;
You must be circumspect in every thing,
Or else your watch, were it as good again,
Would not with time and tide you entertain.

Comparison

This boy an emblem is of a convert,
His watch of the work of grace within his heart,
The watchmaker is Jesus Christ our Lord,
His counsel, the directions of his Word;
Then convert, if thy heart be out of frame,
Of this watchmaker learn to mend the same.
Do not lay ope' thy heart to worldly dust,
Nor let thy graces over-grow with rust,
Be oft' renewed in the' spirit of thy mind,
Or else uncertain thou thy watch wilt find.

XXXIX

UPON A LOOKING-GLASS

n this see thou thy beauty, hast thou any,
Or thy defects, should they be few or many.
Thou may'st, too, here thy spots and freckles see,
Hast thou but eyes, and what their numbers be.
But art thou blind? There is no looking-glass
Can show thee thy defects, thy spots, or face.

Comparison

Unto this glass we may compare the Word,
For that to man advantage doth afford
(Has he a mind to know himself and state),
To see what will be his eternal fate.

But without eyes, alas! how can he see?
Many that seem to look here, blind men be.
This is the reason they so often read
Their judgment there, and do it nothing dread.

XL

OF THE LOVE OF CHRIST

The love of Christ, poor I! may touch upon;
But 'tis unsearchable. O! there is none
Its large dimensions can comprehend
Should they dilate thereon world without end.

When we had sinned, in his zeal he sware,
That he upon his back our sins would bear.
And since unto sin is entailed death,
He vowed for our sins he'd lose his breath.

He did not only say, vow, or resolve,
But to astonishment did so involve
Himself in man's distress and misery,
As for, and with him, both to live and die.

To his eternal fame in sacred story,
We find that he did lay aside his glory,
Stepped from the throne of highest dignity,
Became poor man, did in a manger lie;
Yea, was beholden unto his for bread,
Had, of his own, not where to lay his head;
Though rich, he did for us become thus poor,
That he might make us rich for evermore.

Nor was this but the least of what he did,
But the outside of what he suffered?
God made his blessed son under the law,
Under the curse, which, like the lion's paw,
Did rent and tear his soul for mankind's sin,
More than if we for it in hell had been.
His cries, his tears, and bloody agony,
The nature of his death doth testify.

Nor did he of constraint himself thus give,
For sin, to death, that man might with him live.
He did do what he did most willingly,
He sung, and gave God thanks, that he must die.
But do kings use to die for captive slaves?
Yet we were such when Jesus died to save's.
Yea, when he made himself a sacrifice,
It was that he might save his enemies.

And though he was provoked to retract
His blest resolves for such so good an act,
By the abusive carriages of those
That did both him, his love, and grace oppose;
Yet he, as unconcerned with such things,
Goes on, determines to make captives kings;
Yea, many of his murderers he takes
Into his favour, and them princes makes.

XLI

ON THE CACKLING OF A HEN

he hen, so soon as she an egg doth lay,
(Spreads the fame of her doing what she may.)
About the yard she cackling now doth go,
To tell what 'twas she at her nest did do.

Just thus it is with some professing men,
If they do ought that good is, like our hen
They can but cackle on't where e'er they go,
What their right hand doth their left hand must know.

XLII

UPON AN HOUR-GLASS

his glass, when made, was, by the workman's skill,
The sum of sixty minutes to fulfil.
Time, more nor less, by it will out be spun,
But just an hour, and then the glass is run.

Man's life we will compare unto this glass,
The number of his months he cannot pass;
But when he has accomplished his day,
He, like a vapour, vanisheth away.

XLIII

UPON A SNAIL

She goes but softly, but she goeth sure,
She stumbles not, as stronger creatures do.
Her journey's shorter, so she may endure
Better than they which do much farther go.

She makes no noise, but stilly seizeth on
The flower or herb appointed for her food,
The which she quietly doth feed upon
While others range and glare, but find no good.

And though she doth but very softly go,
However, 'tis not fast nor slow, but sure;
And certainly they that do travel so,
The prize they do aim at they do procure.

Comparison

Although they seem not much to stir, less go,
For Christ that hunger, or from wrath that flee,
Yet what they seek for quickly they come to,
Though it doth seem the farthest off to be.

One act of faith doth bring them to that flower
They so long for, that they may eat and live,
Which, to attain, is not in others power,
Though for it a king's ransom they would give.

Then let none faint, nor be at all dismayed
That life by Christ do seek, they shall not fail
To have it; let them nothing be afraid;
The herb and flower are eaten by the snail.[23]

---

23   If the crawling snail finds food, wherefore do ye doubt, O! ye of little
      faith.—Ed.

XLIV

OF THE SPOUSE OF CHRIST

ho's this that cometh from the wilderness,
Like smokey pillars thus perfum'd with myrrh,
Leaning upon her dearest in distress,
Led into's bosom by the Comforter?

She's clothed with the sun, crowned with twelve stars,
The spotted moon her footstool she hath made.
The dragon her assaults, fills her with jars,
Yet rests she under her Beloved's shade,

But whence was she? what is her pedigree?
Was not her father a poor Amorite?
What was her mother but as others be,
A poor, a wretched, and a sinful Hittite.

Yea, as for her, the day that she was born,
As loathsome, out of doors they did her cast;
Naked and filthy, stinking and forlorn;
This was her pedigree from first to last.

Nor was she pitied in this estate,
All let her lie polluted in her blood:
None her condition did commiserate,
There was no heart that sought to do her good.

Yet she unto these ornaments is come,
Her breasts are fashioned, her hair is grown;
She is made heiress of the best kingdom;
All her indignities away are blown.

Cast out she was, but now she home is taken,
Naked (sometimes), but now, you see, she's cloth'd;
Now made the darling, though before forsaken,
Barefoot, but now as princes' daughters shod.

Instead of filth, she now has her perfumes;
Instead of ignominy, her chains of gold:
Instead of what the beauty most consumes,
Her beauty's perfect, lovely to behold.

Those that attend and wait upon her be
Princes of honour, clothed in white array;
Upon her head's a crown of gold, and she
Eats wheat, honey, and oil, from day to day.

For her beloved, he's the high'st of all,
The only Potentate, the King of kings:
Angels and men do him Jehovah call,
And from him life and glory always springs.

He's white and ruddy, and of all the chief:
His head, his locks, his eyes, his hands, and feet,
Do, for completeness, out-go all belief;
His cheeks like flowers are, his mouth most sweet.

As for his wealth, he is made heir of all;
What is in heaven, what is on earth is his:
And he this lady his joint-heir doth call,
Of all that shall be, or at present is.

Well, lady, well, God has been good to thee;
Thou of an outcast, now art made a queen.
Few, or none, may with thee compared be,
A beggar made thus high is seldom seen.

Take heed of pride, remember what thou art
By nature, though thou hast in grace a share,
Thou in thyself dost yet retain a part
Of thine own filthiness; wherefore beware.

XLV

UPON A SKILFUL PLAYER
OF AN INSTRUMENT

e that can play well on an instrument,
Will take the ear, and captivate the mind
With mirth or sadness; for that it is bent
Thereto, as music in it place doth find.

But if one hears that hath therein no skill,
(As often music lights of such a chance)
Of its brave notes they soon be weary will:
And there are some can neither sing nor dance.

Comparison

Unto him that thus skilfully doth play,
God doth compare a gospel-minister,
That rightly preacheth, and doth godly pray,
Applying truly what doth thence infer.

This man, whether of wrath or grace he preach,
So skilfully doth handle every word;
And by his saying doth the heart so reach,
That it doth joy or sigh before the Lord.

But some there be, which, as the brute, doth lie
Under the Word, without the least advance
Godward; such do despise the ministry;
They weep not at it, neither to it dance.

XLVI

OF MAN BY NATURE

rom God he's a backslider,
Of ways he loves the wider;
With wickedness a sider,
More venom than a spider.

In sin he's a considerer,
A make-bate and divider;
Blind reason is his guider,
The devil is his rider.

XLVII

UPON THE DISOBEDIENT CHILD

Children become, while little, our delights!
When they grow bigger, they begin to fright's.
Their sinful nature prompts them to rebel,
And to delight in paths that lead to hell.
Their parents' love and care they overlook,
As if relation had them quite forsook.
They take the counsels of the wanton's, rather
Than the most grave instructions of a father.
They reckon parents ought to do for them,

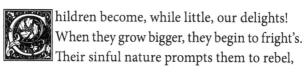

Though they the fifth commandment do contemn;
They snap and snarl if parents them control,
Though but in things most hurtful to the soul.
They reckon they are masters, and that we
Who parents are, should to them subject be!
If parents fain would have a hand in choosing,
The children have a heart will in refusing.
They'll by wrong doings, under parents gather,
And say it is no sin to rob a father.
They'll jostle parents out of place and power,
They'll make themselves the head, and them devour.
How many children, by becoming head,
Have brought their parents to a piece of bread!
Thus they who, at the first, were parents joy,
Turn that to bitterness, themselves destroy.

But, wretched child, how canst thou thus requite
Thy aged parents, for that great delight
They took in thee, when thou, as helpless, lay
In their indulgent bosoms day by day?
Thy mother, long before she brought thee forth,
Took care thou shouldst want neither food nor cloth.
Thy father glad was at his very heart,
Had he to thee a portion to impart.
Comfort they promised themselves in thee,
But thou, it seems, to them a grief wilt be.
How oft, how willingly brake they their sleep,
If thou, their bantling, didst but winch or weep.
Their love to thee was such they could have giv'n,
That thou mightst live, almost their part of heav'n.
But now, behold how they rewarded are!

For their indulgent love and tender care;
All is forgot, this love he doth despise.
They brought this bird up to pick out their eyes.

XLVIII

UPON A SHEET OF WHITE PAPER

This subject is unto the foulest pen,
Or fairest handled by the sons of men.
'Twill also show what is upon it writ,
Be it wisely, or nonsense for want of wit,
Each blot and blur it also will expose
To thy next readers, be they friends or foes.

Comparison

Some souls are like unto this blank or sheet,
Though not in whiteness. The next man they meet,
If wise or fool, debauched or deluder,
Or what you will, the dangerous intruder
May write thereon, to cause that man to err
In doctrine or in life, with blot and blur.
Nor will that soul conceal from who observes,
But show how foul it is, wherein it swerves.
A reading man may know who was the writer,
And, by the hellish nonsense, the inditer.

XLIX

UPON FIRE

ho falls into the fire shall burn with heat;
While those remote scorn from it to retreat.
Yea, while those in it, cry out, O! I burn,
Some farther off those cries to laughter turn.

Comparison

While some tormented are in hell for sin;
On earth some greatly do delight therein.
Yea, while some make it echo with their cry,
Others count it a fable and a lie.[24]

---

24   Fools make a mock at sin. The scorner occupies a proud, an elevated seat, which will sink under him, and crush him down to everlasting destruction. The threatenings and promises of God stand sure for ever.—Ed

Appendix 1

Original Advertisement by the Editor

ome degree of mystery hangs over these Divine Emblems for children, and many years' diligent researches have not enabled me completely to solve it. That they were written by Bunyan, there cannot be the slightest doubt.

'Manner and matter, too, are all his own.'[25]

But no book, under the title of Divine Emblems, is mentioned in any catalogue or advertisements of Bunyan's works, published during his life; nor in those more complete lists printed by his personal friends, immediately after his death. In all these lists, as well as in many advertisement, both before, and shortly after Mr. Bunyan's death, a little book for children is constantly introduced, which, judging from the title, must have been similar to, if not the same as, these Emblems; but the Editor has not been able to discover a copy of the first edition, although every inquiry has been made for it, both in the United Kingdom and America. It was

25   Bunyan's poem in the Holy War.

advertised in 1688, as Country Rhymes for Children, upon seventy-four things.[26] It is also advertised, in the same year, as A Book for Boys and Girls, or Country Rhymes for Children, price 6d.[27] In 1692, it is included in Charles Doe's catalogue table of all Mr. Bunyan's books, appended to The Struggler for their preservation, No. 36; Meditations on seventy-four things, published in 1685, and not reprinted during the author's life. In Charles Doe's second catalogue of all Mr. Bunyan's books, appended to the first edition of the Heavenly Footman, March 1698, it is No. 37. A Book for Boys and Girls, or Country Rhymes for Children, in verse, on seventy-four things. This catalogue describes every work, word for word, as it is in the several title pages. In 1707 it had reached a third edition, and was 'ornamented with cuts';[28] and the title is altered to A Book for Boys and Girls, or Temporal Things Spiritualized, with cuts. In 1720, it was advertised, 'price, bound, 6d.'[29] In Keach's Glorious Lover, it is advertised by Marshall, in 12mo. price 1s. In 1724, it assumed its present title, and from that time was repeatedly advertised as Divine Emblems, or Temporal Things Spiritualized, fitted for the use of boys and girls, adorned with cuts.

By indefatigable exertions, my excellent friend and brother collector of old English bibles, James Dix, Esq., Bristol, has just discovered and presented to me

26 On the leaf following the title to One Thing is Needful, &c., by John Bunyan, 1688. A rare little 32mo, published by the author, in possession of the Editor.

27 At the end of Grace Abounding, the sixth edition, and also in The Work of Jesus Christ as an Advocate, by Bunyan, 1688.

28 Advertised in the eighth edition of Solomon's Temple Spiritualized.

29 In Youth Directed and Instructed—a curious little book for children.

the second edition of this very rare little volume, in fine preservation, from which it appears, that in 1701, the title page was altered from Country Rhymes and Meditations, to A Book for Boys and Girls, or Temporal Things Spiritualized. It has no cuts, but, with that exception, it contains exactly the same subjects as the subsequent editions published under the more popular title of Divine Emblems.

The only difficulty that remains is to discover seventy-four meditations in the forty-nine Emblems. This may be readily done, if the subjects of meditation are drawn out. Thus, the first emblem contains meditations on two things, the Barren Fig-tree, and God's Vineyard. So the second has a meditation on the Lark and the Fowler, and another on the comparison between the Fowler and Satan. Upon this plan, the volume contains exactly seventy-four meditations.

Under the title of Divine Emblems, it has passed through a multitude of editions, and many thousand copies have been circulated. It was patronized in those early efforts of the Religious Tract Society, which have been so abundantly blessed in introducing wholesome food to the young, instead of the absurd romances which formerly poisoned the infant and youthful mind.

Among these numerous editions, two deserve special notice. The first of these was published in 1757, 'on a curious paper, and good letter, with new cuts.' It has a singular preface, signed J. D., addressed 'to the great Boys, in folio, and the little ones in coats.' The first eight pages are occupied with a dissertation on the origin of language, perhaps arising from a line in the dialogue between a sinner and spider, 'My name entailed is to my creation.' In this preface, he learnedly attempts to prove that language was the gift of God by revelation, and not a gradual acquirement of man as his wants multiplied. The other remarkable edition was published about 1790.[30] It is, both the text and cuts, printed from copperplate engravings, very handsomely executed. This is an honour conferred upon very few authors;[31] nor was it ever conferred upon one more worthy the highest veneration of man than is the immortal allegorist.

The number of editions which have been printed of these little engaging poems, is a proof of the high estimation in which they have been held for nearly one hundred and seventy years; and the great rarity of the early copies shows the eager interest with which they have been read by children until utterly destroyed.

The cuts were at first exceedingly coarse and rude, but were much improved in the more modern copies. Those to Mason's edition are handsome. The engraver has dressed all his actors in the costume of the time of George the Third; the women with hooped petticoats and high head dresses; clergymen with five or six tier wigs; men with cocked hats and queues; and female servants with mob caps. That to Emblem Fifteen, upon the sacraments, is peculiarly droll; the artist, forgetting that the author was a Baptist, represents a baby brought to the font to be christened! and two persons kneeling before the body of our Lord!

 – GEO. OFFOR.

---

30 Square 24mo., by Bennet, Gurney, and others, without date.
31 Sturt engraved the Book of Common Prayer; some French artists elegantly etched two of their devotional books; and Pyne engraved the texts of Horace and Virgil with beautiful vignettes.

Appendix 2

John Bunyan's Original Preface

ourteous reader,
The title page will show, if there thou look,
Who are the proper subjects of this book.
They're boys and girls of all sorts and degrees,
From those of age to children on the knees.
Thus comprehensive am I in my notions,
They tempt me to it by their childish motions.
We now have boys with beards, and girls that be
Big[32] as old women, wanting gravity.
Then do not blame me, 'cause I thus describe them.
Flatter I may not, lest thereby I bribe them
To have a better judgment of themselves,
Than wise men have of babies on their shelves.[33]
Their antic tricks, fantastic modes, and way,
Show they, like very boys and girls, do play
With all the frantic fopperies of this age,

---

32   Altered to 'huge' in the Emblems, 1724.
33   A familiar phrase, denoting persons who have been always frivolous
      and childish, or those who have passed into second childhood. 'On
      the shelf' is a common saying of ladies when they are too old to get
      married.—Ed.

And that in open view, as on a stage;
Our bearded men do act like beardless boys;
Our women please themselves with childish toys.
Our ministers, long time, by word and pen,
Dealt with them, counting them not boys, but men.
Thunderbolts they shot at them and their toys,
But hit them not, 'cause they were girls and boys.
The better charg'd, the wider still they shot,
Or else so high, these dwarfs they touched not.
Instead of men, they found them girls and boys,
Addict to nothing as to childish toys.

Wherefore, good reader, that I save them may,
I now with them the very dotterel[34] play;
And since at gravity they make a tush,
My very beard I cast behind a bush;
And like a fool stand fing'ring of their toys,
And all to show them they are girls and boys.

Nor do I blush, although I think some may
Call me a baby, 'cause I with them play.
I do't to show them how each fingle-fangle
On which they doting are, their souls entangle,
As with a web, a trap, a gin, or snare;
And will destroy them, have they not a care.

Paul seemed to play the fool, that he might gain
Those that were fools indeed, if not in grain;[35]
And did it by their things, that they might know
Their emptiness, and might be brought unto

---

34   The name of a bird that mimics gestures.—Ed.
35   Indelible, as when raw material is dyed before it is wove, every grain
      receives the dye.—Ed.

What would them save from sin and vanity,
A noble act, and full of honesty.
Yet he nor I would like them be in vice,
While by their playthings I would them entice,
To mount their thoughts from what are childish toys,
To heaven, for that's prepared for girls and boys.
Nor do I so confine myself to these,
As to shun graver things; I seek to please
Those more compos'd with better things than toys;
Though thus I would be catching girls and boys.

Wherefore, if men have now a mind to look,
Perhaps their graver fancies may be took
With what is here, though but in homely rhymes:
But he who pleases all must rise betimes.
Some, I persuade me, will be finding fault,
Concluding, here I trip, and there I halt:
No doubt some could those grovelling notions raise
By fine-spun terms, that challenge might the bays.
But should all men be forc'd to lay aside
Their brains that cannot regulate the tide
By this or that man's fancy, we should have
The wise unto the fool become a slave.
What though my text seems mean, my morals be
Grave, as if fetch'd from a sublimer tree.
And if some better handle[36] can a fly,
Than some a text, why should we then deny
Their making proof, or good experiment,
Of smallest things, great mischiefs to prevent?

---

36   For this use of the word 'handle,' see Jeremiah 2:8. 'They that handle
      the law.'—Ed.

Wise Solomon did fools to piss-ants[37] send,
To learn true wisdom, and their lies to mend.
Yea, God by swallows, cuckoos, and the ass,[38]
Shows they are fools who let that season pass,
Which he put in their hand, that to obtain
Which is both present and eternal gain.

I think the wiser sort my rhymes may slight,
But what care I, the foolish will delight
To read them, and the foolish God has chose,
And doth by foolish things their minds compose,
And settle upon that which is divine;
Great things, by little ones, are made to shine.

I could, were I so pleas'd, use higher strains:
And for applause on tenters[39] stretch my brains.
But what needs that? the arrow, out of sight,
Does not the sleeper, nor the watchman fright;
To shoot too high doth but make children gaze,
'Tis that which hits the man doth him amaze.

And for the inconsiderableness
Of things, by which I do my mind express,
May I by them bring some good thing to pass,
As Samson, with the jawbone of an ass;
Or as brave Shamgar, with his ox's goad
(Both being things not manly, nor for war in mode),
I have my end, though I myself expose
To scorn; God will have glory in the close.

---

37 This word, with pismire and emmet, has become obsolete. 'Ant' is
the term now universally used.—Ed.
38 See Psalm 84:3; Leviticus 11:16; Numbers 20.
39 A machine used in the manufacture of cloth, on which it is
stretched.—Ed.

Additional updated, classic titles available from Aneko Press:

About the Author

ohn Bunyan was born November 1628, in Elstow, England. A celebrated English minister and preacher, he wrote *The Pilgrim's Progress* (1678), the book that was the most characteristic expression of the Puritan religious outlook. His other works include doctrinal and controversial writings; a spiritual autobiography, *Grace Abounding* (1666); and the allegory *The Holy War* (1682).

ften disguised as something that would help him,
evil accompanies Christian on his journey to
the Celestial City. As you walk with him, you'll
begin to identify today's many religious pitfalls. These are
presented by men such as Pliable, who turns back at the
Slough of Despond; and Ignorance, who believes he's a true
follower of Christ when he's really only trusting in himself.
Each character represented in this allegory is intentionally
and profoundly accurate in its depiction of what we see
all around us, and unfortunately, what we too often see in
ourselves. But while Christian is injured and nearly killed,
he eventually prevails to the end. So can you.

The best part of this book is the Bible verses added to
the text. The original *Pilgrim's Progress* listed the Bible
verse references, but the verses themselves are so impactful
when tied to the scenes in this allegory, that they are now
included within the text of this book. The text is tweaked
just enough to make it readable today, for the young and the
old. Youngsters in particular will be drawn to the original
illustrations included in this wonderful classic.

Available where books are sold

hat if you were able to see your life from a spiritual perspective and see the actual reality of the verse above? How does our enemy, Diabolus, plan and carry out his attacks? How do his demons help, and what are their objectives? Why and how must we petition Emmanuel to get His attention and help in this great, holy war?

Written four years after *The Pilgrim's Progress*, John Bunyan followed up with this second allegorical classic, which has touched hearts and minds of readers for generations. The epicenter of this book is the town of Mansoul, its people (such as Conscience, Self-Denial, and Do-Right), and its gates (Eye-gate, Ear-gate, Mouth-gate, Nose-gate, and Feel-gate). The attack by Diabolus and his demons, all of whom have appropriate names, is carefully planned and executed. As still happens to men today, Mansoul fell hard. Emmanuel is of course willing to help, but can only do so on special, seemingly strict terms. As you watch this intense battle unfold, you'll be emboldened to fight with new vigilance, to guard the gates with tenacity, and to rely on Emmanuel's sovereignty like never before.

Available where books are sold

Printed in Great Britain
by Amazon

61855913R00073